leapfrog

Rhyme
Time

# Bathtime
# Rap

First published in 2008 by
Franklin Watts
338 Euston Road
London
NW1 3BH

Franklin Watts Australia
Level 17/207 Kent Street
Sydney
NSW 2000

A CIP catalogue record for this book is available
from the British Library.

ISBN 978 0 7496 7951 4 (hbk)
ISBN 978 0 7496 7963 7 (pbk)

**Series Editor:** Jackie Hamley
**Editor:** Melanie Palmer
**Series Advisor:** Dr Barrie Wade
**Series Designer:** Peter Scoulding

Printed in China

Franklin Watts is a division of
Hachette Children's Books,
an Hachette Livre UK company.
www.hachettelivre.co.uk

# Bathtime Rap

by Rosalind K. Adam

Illustrated by Neil Chapman

W
FRANKLIN WATTS
LONDON•SYDNEY

# I pull off my shoes,
# my jumper and vest.

Mum turns the taps
while I take off the rest.

I pour in the soap and watch the foam grow.

Then I test the water
with my biggest toe.

11

I throw in my duck and
my shiny white boat ...

13

... and the sailing ship
that won't stay afloat.

# Then in goes Giraffe

and the red rubber dog,

and best of all Freddie,
the squeaky, green frog.

I squirt them ...

and shoot them ...

and sink them all –

– except for Giraffe.
He's much too tall.

I refill my bottle
right up to the top,

and shoot at the bubbles
until they all pop.

27

Now it's time to get out.
I put the toys on the shelf.

29

30

Oh no! I've forgotten
to wash myself!

Leapfrog Rhyme Time has been specially designed to fit the requirements of the Literacy Framework. It offers real books for beginner readers by top authors and illustrators.

**Other Leapfrog titles also available:**

**Leapfrog Fairy Tales**

A selection of favourite fairy tales, simply retold.

**Leapfrog**

Fun, original stories by top authors and illustrators.

**For more details go to:**

www.franklinwatts.co.uk